Does Love Grow at Christmas?

Written By Eric G. Burstock

Illustrated by Kimberly Merritt

Scripture taken from the New King James Version®. Copyright © 1982 by Thomas Nelson. Used by permission. All rights reserved.

ISBN 979-8-9859459-0-4 (paperback)
     979-8-9859459-1-1 (hardback)

Editing, formatting and design by ChristianEditingandDesign.com
Illustrated by Kimberly Merritt

Dedicated to our grandchildren:
Samuel Harding Davison, born 2017,
and Juliette Paige Davison, born 2021.

I wrote this book especially for young children. Early readers will enjoy reading it themselves, or the adult in their life can read it to them. Designed to be read on Christmas Eve or Christmas morning, it's guaranteed to become a favorite Christmas tradition for families during Christmas time.

— Eric G. Burstock

Does love grow at Christmas?

Yes, love grows so big at Christmas!

we love to celebrate and are so
excited and happy at Christmas!

Loves grows at Christmas because . . . we love to eat Christmas cookies, candy, and tasty foods. They are yummy in our tummies!

Loves grows at Christmas because . . .

we love to put ornaments on our Christmas tree!

Loves grows at Christmas because . . .

we love to wear our Christmas pajamas!

Loves grows at Christmas because . . .

the love of Jesus makes Christmas so special!

Loves grows at Christmas because . . .

before we close our eyes to sleep, we know Jesus loves us and lives in our hearts!

CPSIA information can be obtained
at www.ICGtesting.com
Printed in the USA
LVHW071344120522
718523LV00002B/21